8.7.72

Multiple Sclerosis And Me

Multiple Sclerosis And Me

By

M. H. GREENBLATT

With a Foreword by

Martin M. Mandel, M.D.

CHARLES C THOMAS • PUBLISHER
Springfield • Illinois • U.S.A.

Published and Distributed Throughout the World by

CHARLES C THOMAS • PUBLISHER
Bannerstone House
301-327 East Lawrence Avenue, Springfield, Illinois, U.S.A.
Natchez Plantation House
735 North Atlantic Boulevard, Fort Lauderdale, Florida, U.S.A.

ISBN 0-398-02300-X

Library of Congress Catalog Card Number: 72-180824

With THOMAS BOOKS careful attention is given to all details of manufacturing and design. It is the Publisher's desire to present books that are satisfactory as to their physical qualities and artistic possibilities and appropriate for their particular use. THOMAS BOOKS will be true to those laws of quality that assure a good name and good will.

Printed in the United States of America
R-1

For my daughters, Harriet and Barbara

Foreword

PHYSICIANS are usually preoccupied with the medical aspects of multiple sclerosis and frequently fail to appreciate the emotional responses of a multiple sclerosis patient. Doctor Greenblatt, in this unique presentation, depicts his fears and feelings from the onset of his illness until the present time.

I have known the author since high school and undergraduate days at the University of Pennsylvania. During recent years, I have had the privilege of attending Doctor Greenblatt as his neurologist; and I have shared his problems and given direction to him and his family.

This book will be of value not only to the patient afflicted with multiple sclerosis but also to the physician who treats this illness. Both will obtain insights and, more importantly, the patient will be able to adjust to his illness more adequately. The author has also demonstrated his productivity by contributing articles to music and literary journals as well as publishing a book on mathematical puzzles.

MARTIN M. MANDEL, M.D.

Preface

I AM one of the nearly half a million people in the United States who have multiple sclerosis. If one looks in the dictionary to find out what multiple sclerosis is, one discovers that MS is a syndrome – that is, it is a collection of symptoms, all of which appear to be related. People who have many or all of these symptoms may be diagnosed as having multiple sclerosis. There are no symptoms which are symptomatic of MS and MS alone. The fact that any one symptom may be characteristic of many different ailments makes diagnosis of MS rather difficult. A diagnosis by a skilled neurologist is required.

There have been a great many statistical studies of MS patients. Patients have been classified by educational level, by geographical place of origin, by race and by many other characteristics. Many statistical correlations have been discovered, and a diagnosis of MS is very often based on these statistical correlations.

Much has been written about MS either by statisticians or by physicians or by clinicians. This book is an attempt to give a report of the disease, multiple sclerosis, from a patient's point of view and to describe some of that patient's activities before the diagnosis of MS.

I have MS, and because of this, I feel that I am in a

particularly good position to describe the attitudes, actions and reactions of at least one MS patient. This book is addressed primarily to other MS patients, and some of them may discover that their own symptoms are not unique.

I have attempted to include items which are pertinent, interesting or perhaps both.

It is hoped that this book will be of interest not only to MS patients but also to those who do not have MS themselves but who are concerned with MS. This latter group can include therapists, nurses, physicians and so forth.

Contents

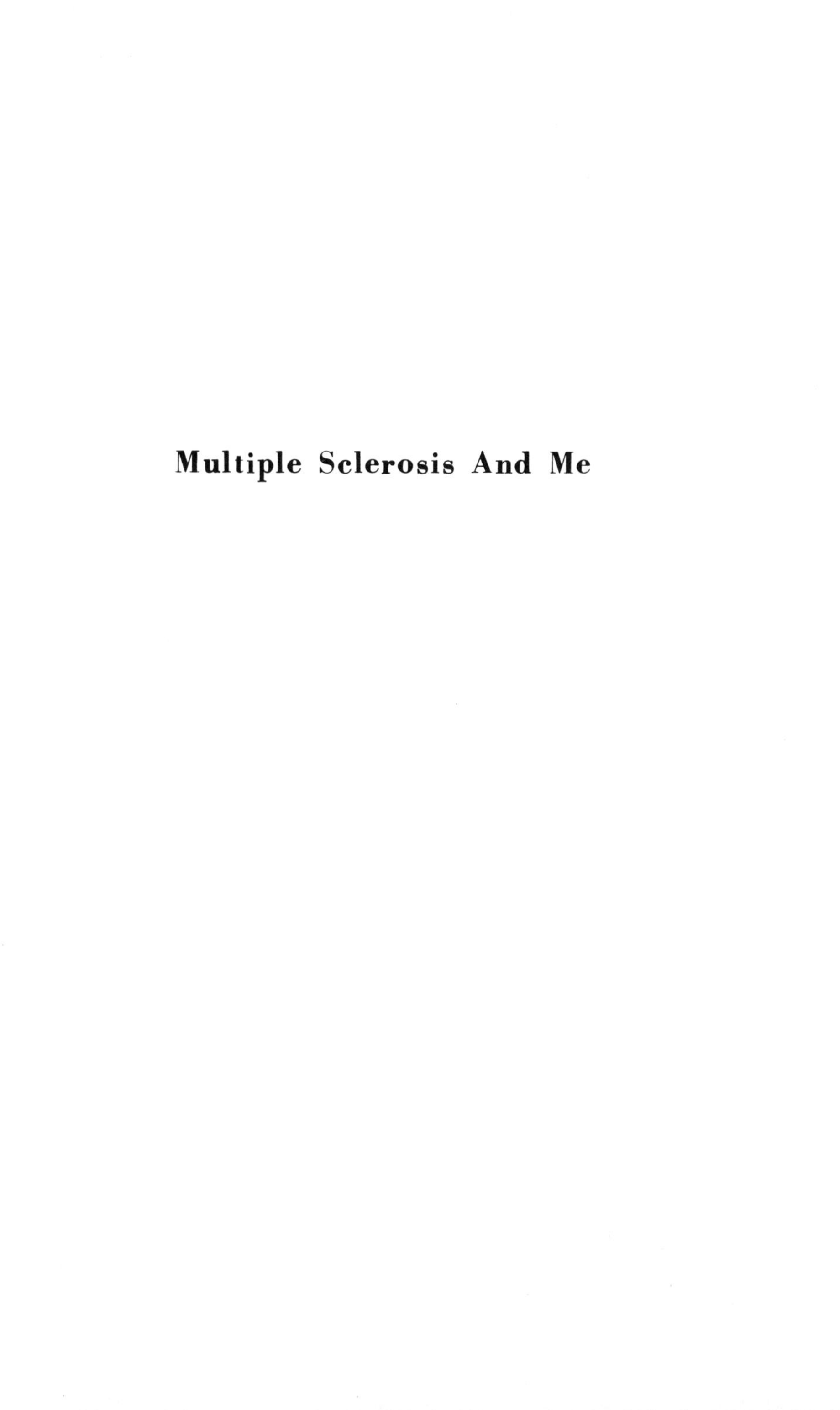

Multiple Sclerosis And Me

1

The Beginning

IN 1951 (a year deeply engraved in my memory), I first heard the diagnosis, "I think you have multiple sclerosis." The speaker was Dr. Yaskin, a well-known neurologist in Philadelphia. The reasons for my visit to Dr. Yaskin are briefly the following:

I was 29 years old. I had graduated as a physicist from the University of Pennsylvania and was, at that time, working for RCA in Princeton, New Jersey. In most respects, I seemed to be a perfectly normal fellow. I had not had more than the usual number of childhood diseases, and none of those that I did have had been unusually severe.

I had started to work for the RCA Laboratories in 1948. I noticed in the latter half of 1951 that when I walked along the hall of the laboratory, my left foot would slap the floor. In a normal walk, the heel touches the ground first, and then the whole front of the foot is lowered slowly, gradually and controllably to the floor. But in my case, I didn't seem to have good control over the front part of my left foot. The fact that my left foot slapped against the floor was annoying, but not a big enough thing to make me want to see a neurologist. So I did that which is recommended by so many people, and even by many physicians – I simply waited to see if it would go away. (I cannot help feeling that this attitude is precisely the one which an ostrich would have; let's pretend it isn't there and perhaps it'll go away.) In November of 1951, I happened to have a mild case of the flu, and when the local doctor came to visit me, I asked about this foot-slap on the floor. He looked at my face and asked me to smile as broadly as possible and to show him all my teeth. (Apparently, this is one of the broad neurological tests which shows whether or not the muscles on both sides of your face are evenly balanced.) The local physician apparently didn't like what he saw, because he suggested that I go to see a neurologist; in fact, he suggested Dr. Yaskin. So within a few weeks, I was down at Dr. Yaskin's office.

Dr. Yaskin gave me a thorough office-type neurological examination. (The meaning of the word "office-type" is simply that there are many types of neurological examinations which simply cannot be conducted in a physician's office.) After he had used the pins, needles, cotton and hard rubber banging instruments, he then skillfully led me to report any significant neurological happenings during the past several years. These neurological findings were particularly disturbing in my case.

When I was about 25 years old, I had diplopia. (Diplopia is a medical term for what is known as double vision.) The difficulty here was that a nice neat image would be focused on the retina of each eye. Then the brain is supposed to fuse these two images so that we have stereoptical vision of a single scene. The difficulty in the case of diplopia is that the two images do not fuse. The effect is that one sees two distinct images of anything one is looking at. I have often wondered what would happen if one used a color-corrected prism so as to shift the position of one image on the retina so that the fusion of the two images would take place in the brain. There is no doubt in my mind that this can be done, but it may be that the amount of shift required in the two images is different from day to day. In this case, one would need a variable shifting lens over one eye. It would be difficult, but not impossible, to do this, and it may be that not much would be gained by practice. The fact that I had had diplopia was an indication that I was a very likely candidate for multiple sclerosis. At the present time (1969), it would probably not be particularly helpful to know that one is a likely candidate for multiple sclerosis; but one day in the future, it may be a very valuable bit of information.

Not only had I had diplopia when I was 25 years old, but I had also had dysarthria, which also goes under the more common name of "cotton-mouth." At about that time, I was an instructor in physics at the University of Pennsylvania. Normally, I could talk to the class in a perfectly normal manner. However sometimes, I would come across a perfectly ordinary word which I had great difficulty in pronouncing correctly. Just as all symptoms of my double vision disappeared in a matter of a few months, so all symptoms of the dysarthria also disappeared within a few months.

At about this time, another symptom struck. My handwriting, which was normally neat and regular, would suddenly degenerate into a childlike scrawl. I was unable to correlate this degeneration of my handwriting with any external event. This time, as with the previous two symptoms, I went to the student health service to try to find out what was happening. I can still remember the doctor as he examined me. He had me sitting down at the desk writing the sentence, "Round and round the rugged rock, the ragged rascal ran." (This is apparently one of the multiple-duty phrases that the doctors carry around in their bag of tricks. It is useful in analyzing dysarthria and undoubtedly a great many other pathologies.) The doctor's final words were, "Well, come back in six months, and we'll see if it's still there." I hope the reader and the medical profession will pardon me if I say, "Well, damn it! I don't need you to tell me if I still have the symptoms six months from now!"

These were about all of the symptoms that occurred to me when I was about 25 years old – diplopia, dysarthria, difficulty in writing. As of today, almost any doctor would consider multiple sclerosis to be a very likely choice for the pathology of a person afflicted with these symptoms. I cannot bring myself to believe that things have changed so much since I went to school; I suspect the medical people I spoke to were not on their toes. After Dr. Yaskin had elicited all this history, he said, "I think you have multiple sclerosis. But I would like to check a little bit further on this. Can you come to the hospital where we can do more tests than I can do here?"

So I went to the Graduate Hospital of the University of Pennsylvania. There I was x-rayed from more angles than I knew existed. I had a spinal tap performed. I had my fingernails flicked by more people than I thought would do such a thing. After ten days of such tests, Dr. Yaskin reported to me: "We have tested and you do NOT have syphillis of the spine. You do NOT have a brain tumor." Then he proceeded to name a long list of other neurological diseases which I also did NOT have. He finally wound up saying, "The only thing, then, that is not ruled out is multiple sclerosis. This is my diagnosis." "Shucks," I said, "I was hoping that I had a brain tumor or something operable of that sort – something that you could cure easily." Dr. Yaskin's answer was, "You're far better off with multiple sclerosis than you would be if you had a brain tumor." From what little I have seen, I suspect that he was correct.

One curious little thing happened to me while I was in the hospital. One day, I was given a spinal tap. Now, the description of a spinal tap is far worse than the actual experience. The purpose of the spinal tap is to withdraw the spinal fluid so that they can then do the colloidal gold test on the fluid to test for syphillis of the spine. After they had taken the fluid (I didn't have quite enough nerve to say, "Is that all?"), the doctor left. I got up off the bed and walked out of the room. As soon as I had gotten in the hall, a nurse saw me and shrieked, "Oh, Dr. Greenblatt, please, you have to get back in bed!" After she got me in bed, she called the doctor and he came around to see me. "You see," he said, "we have performed statistical studies and find that 50 percent of all patients who get up and walk around immediately after a spinal tap get headaches. And we find that half of the patients who rest afterwards, do not get headaches."

At this point, I would like to mention that, at the time, I felt that no one could look at me and tell that I had multiple sclerosis. All mechanical devices associated with me appeared to be working fine; I was able to walk perfectly normally; I talked almost normally; I wrote almost normally, etcetera. After I had been in the hospital for a few days, I was talking to my fellow roommate. He said, "You know, when I first saw you, I thought you were drunk or something like that. You seemed to stagger as you walked."

All this was in spite of the fact that I thought I was walking perfectly normally.

2

The Next Sixteen Years

THE progress in my case, of this most inconsistent and variable disease, has been (if I may, myself, be inconsistent) almost "classical." My condition has deteriorated – not in any sudden or obviously noticeable way – but there is no doubt that it has deteriorated. Among the most significant effects is the obvious one that I can no longer walk. I can, however, hold my dictating microphone about as well as I could ten years ago. (However, sixteen years ago, I didn't need a dictaphone. I could simply write what I wanted to.) Of course, when one's ability to walk is thus materially decreased, the ability to check on many other things is also decreased. I wouldn't know what to say about my sense of balance. It doesn't seem to be much of a trick at all to balance one's self in a wheelchair. As far as strength in various muscles is concerned, I am sure that what I have left has been greatly reduced from what it was, but it seems to be completely adequate for low level "bumbling around the house."

In addition to the simple strength of the muscles, another important concept is related to the sense of kinesthesia – that is, the sense of knowing where a particular muscle is without actually looking at it. A typical way the neurologists have of testing for that (among other things) is to have you close your eyes, stretch out your hand and then bring your forefinger over to the tip of your nose. Inability to do this is not a symptom of multiple sclerosis but is rather a symptom of reduced kinesthetic sense.

I do not recall any single day during the past sixteen years when I was not able to do something that I was able to do the day before. But the disease, MS, progresses in such a slow manner that changes are often not noticeable. The only way I can detect changes is to try to think back to five or ten years ago and imagine what I could do then.

It may be that people who have had MS for a long time (whom I call seasoned MS veterans) may not show the deleterious effects of the disease, in the same sense that professional topers don't show the effects of drunkenness. About ten or twenty years ago, a survey was made which tried to show that a given amount of alcohol in the bloodstream of a human being would affect all people about the same. The obvious question is, "But there are some people who drink all day long and they apparently show no effects of drunkenness at all, yet a novice will take one single glass of whiskey, and he will stagger all over and never be able to follow a straight line." The explanation in the article was that the old professional toper is aware of his limitations and doesn't even try to walk a straight line; all he does is sit at the table. You're not going to get him to move for anything!

In the same way, it may be that MS veterans simply do not try to do anything beyond their abilities.

My present situation is that the muscles in my arms and legs are apparently just falling away. I cannot walk or stand; I have great difficulty holding anything in my hands. However my ability to push a button on my dictaphone machine is apparently not affected; neither is, I hope, the workings of my brain. I have, for example, some difficulty in turning pages of a book but this slight difficulty seems to be a rather trivial price to pay for the joys of being able to read.

After Dr. Yaskin had made his diagnosis, he also gave me some suggestions on therapy. I was to take 1 cc of liver extract to be injected into my buttocks once a week. I was also to take about 1 cc of histamine which could be subcutaneously injected once a week. (At that time, my inabilities due to multiple sclerosis were superficial – not at all obvious to an untrained person. As I stood over the stove boiling the syringe, needle and tongs, I used to humorously refer to them as "my MS kit.")

Sometime around 1954, Dr. Yaskin died. I had visited him once or twice since the diagnosis, and I wasn't quite sure what I should do now. A friend of mine at Princeton University suggested that he had been going to see a neurologist in New York City. He suggested that I might go to see him also. I took my friend's advice, and I saw Dr. Brickner in New York City for about a year. After about a year or so, Dr. Brickner had a heart attack and retired from activity in the field of neurology.

Now I began to feel as if I were a pariah of some sort. Both medical men that I had seen were now retired – one, by reason of death, and the other, by reason of a heart attack. I felt that it was only fair of me to warn the next medical man that I asked to help me that it might be a little dangerous taking care of me. (I am glad to say that my suspicions were not borne out. I have seen two medical people since then, and neither has suffered in any such severe manner.)

After Dr. Brickner retired, I went to see Dr. Schwartz in Philadelphia. I saw Dr. Schwartz for some time when, finally, in 1963 or so, I became aware of the fact that one of my high school classmates was now a practicing neurologist. Since then, I have been under the care of Dr. M. Mandel.

The progress of the disease since 1951 has been roughly the following: Up until 1959, I walked without a cane or any other appliance. My walk was not always smooth, but I always got where I was going. In 1959, I started to use a cane. Sometimes, the cane was absolutely necessary, and at other times, it was merely a walking stick. In 1962, I started to use Canadian canes (the type cane which has an extension which fits onto the forearm). By 1964, I was using the Canadian canes about half the time and a wheelchair the other half of the time. Shortly after that, things had deteriorated to a point where I could not walk with the Canadian canes at all. I was completely dependent on the wheelchair for locomotion. I began to wonder how much further downhill I could possibly go, and I asked Dr. Mandel. He said that it looked as if I had gone most of the way downhill already, and he didn't think I could go much further in a downward direction. In a sense, I believe this is so. It would be very difficult for me to find something that I could not do today that I was able to do a year ago. I suspect that if there has been deterioration within the past year, then it can only be detected with a fairly fine measurement.

This brings my medical history more or less up to the present. I am able to stand and lock my knees for as long as ten seconds at a time, if someone will lift me up to that position. I cannot raise myself to a standing position by my own efforts. My mental abilities appear to be unimpaired when compared with the same abilities before MS.

Since MS has severely curtailed my physical activities, I now have the opportunity to read many of the things that I have always wanted to read and to write those things that I have always wanted to write. My first efforts in the field of writing were to put together a book on mathematics at the sharp high school level. It is a book of mathematical puzzles, pleasantries and observations. The fact that my first effort was moderately successful has spurred me on to try writing in a few other fields. (This book is almost a natural for a person who (a) has multiple sclerosis and (b) who likes to write.) The rest of this book will be concerned with mild observations that I, a MS patient, have made. Please be forewarned that these are the observations of a layman (albeit, I hope, an intelligent one) and not a physician.

One day, after my neurological symptoms were well established and my difficulty in walking was only beginning to become apparent, the following curious episode occurred. I was, at the time, able to walk although I knew I had MS but I hadn't the vaguest idea of how fast I would go downhill. On this particular day, I started to walk upstairs. Normally, at that time, I could lift one leg and place it on the next step. Then I could move the other leg up to that step and in this way, I could manage the whole flight of steps. (I didn't get there fast, but I got there.) On the particular day in question, I had great difficulty in picking my leg up to the next step. I started to think to myself that this must be what it feels like to go downhill rapidly. Somehow, I managed to get myself all the way upstairs and I was so enervated by the procedure that I immediately plunked myself into bed. Once I was in bed, my wife decided to take my temperature – just for kicks. It turned out that I had 99.6°F of temperature, but as we soon found out, even such a trivial excess of temperature can be extremely debilitating to an MS patient. I can still remember how thankful my wife and I were that my suddenly poor performance was due to a slight excess in temperature rather than to a general downhill progress of the disease. One's sense of values certainly can change.

3

Some Experiments That Didn't Work Out

I AM having great difficulty writing this chapter; part of the reason is that it is only since the last century that MS has been recognized as a disease unto itself and part of the reason is due to the fact that such a vigorous attack has been mounted against its protean manifestations. Because of the vigorous attack on the mystery, the relative importance of some of the finer points of the disease are changing. (I have always thought that "the guy who never made a mistake never did anything" and that every field of human knowledge has its share of "boo-boos." The medical profession is not immune to that observation.)

Among the stories that seem to be based more on fancy than on fact is the one concerning ACTH (ACTH is an acronym for adrenocorticotropic hormone). The adrenal glands are situated toward the back of the body and are on top of the kidneys. The function of ACTH is to stimulate the outer covering of the adrenal glands – the cortex – and to try to get the adrenal glands to put out its own hormones. In the early days of experimentation with ACTH, it was said, in some scientific journal, that taking ACTH has a tendency to increase the irritability of the person taking the drug. I have often taken ACTH and have never noticed any change at all in my irritability. Perhaps this says something about my normal amount of irritability. (Perhaps I am normally so irritable that I couldn't possibly become more so.) However, as was once said, "Once such a notion appears in a scientific journal, people constantly refer to it and not even a Papal Encyclical will stop people from referring to it." So, I warn everyone who happens to be taking ACTH, that the mere fact that you are taking ACTH may be enough reason for some people to accuse you of being irritable and cranky.

I have a friend who takes ACTH and he tells me that he feels somewhat more irritable when he takes it. Maybe it affects different people differently.

ON THE USE OF ORINASE®

In England, the journal *Lancet* is roughly the equivalent of the *Journal of the American Medical Association.* An article appeared in *Lancet,* in the 1950's, in which it was indicated that Orinase could be used to cure multiple sclerosis. Not unexpectedly, attempts were made to duplicate these remarkable results here in the United States. The experiments were done at the University of Minnesota Medical School, and they were able to duplicate the results reported in *Lancet!* The data reported in *Lancet* was that MS patients, when given some tolbutamide (the generic name of Orinase) were almost miraculously cured of all effects of MS. Tolbutamide is a drug which is sometimes known as "oral insulin." For some people, the main effect is that it causes the pancreas to produce a little more insulin. It has this effect mostly on people who were adults at the time that diabetes became apparent. The results obtained at the University of Minnesota were published in the *Journal of the American Medical Association.* The Sunday *New York Times* carried an article in the "News of the Week in Review" section saying that the results achieved at the University of Minnesota Medical School were greeted by MS patients with cries of exhultation, dancing and thankfulness. Results were described in which the MS patients threw their previously required canes into the air.

I excitedly read the article and as soon as I was able, called my neurologist to see if he didn't agree that this was a wonderful result. He was very lukewarm to the entire idea. He finally suggested, "Well, you can take the tolbutamide if you want to. I don't think it will hurt you, but I don't think it will do you a bit of good, either." I took the tolbutamide for about half a year and finally convinced myself that the articles in *Lancet* and in the *Journal of the American Medical Association* were somehow mysteriously wrong. (I confess I still find it difficult to understand why my neurologist was able to surmise that the whole thing was unlikely and the editors of the *Journal of the American Medical Association* were not able to determine this same thing. I believe the fault in the experiments reported in both journals was that the number of patients involved was not a statistically valid sample. The results were undoubtedly accurately reported, but the "cures" may have been due to naturally occurring remissions.)

There have been many different kinds of medical therapy that have been tried to cure MS. Most of them have had very little effect on the progress of the disease. On the other hand, they have been all tried in perfectly good conscience and with very acceptable reasoning. For example, it has been suggested by some medical men that MS may be due to the fact that blood clots settle in different places in the brain. In order to prevent the formation of blood clots, Dicumarol® (a drug which prevents the formation of blood clots) has been suggested for MS patients. The results obtained with

Dicumarol also have not been earth-shattering. Breathing pure carbon dioxide has also been tried as a medical therapy for MS.

Shortly after MS made its presence known in me, I developed a central scotoma in my left eye. At the time, it looked as if new symptoms were going to develop at a fast and furious rate. The medical man that I happened to wind up with suggested the use of amyl nitrite (amyl nitrite is a drug which is inhaled and which has a marked effect in enlarging the blood vessels). Its use with patients with certain types of heart disease is almost standard. Its effect on MS is somewhat less dramatic. When I say it is somewhat less dramatic, all I mean to imply is that it does not appear to have any overall curative effect. On the other hand, I can report that the central scotoma in my left eye is no longer there. This brings up a question nearly as classic as "The lady or the tiger?" Was the disappearance of the scotoma due to the amyl nitrite, or in spite of it, or would it have gone away by itself?

4

Some Statistical Surveys*

STATISTICAL surveys have recently been becoming more and more popular. Of course, the conclusions will be valid only when the statistics are valid. There is no guarantee that valid statistics will give rise to a valid conclusion. I must digress at this point to mention that I once came across a very clever example of valid statistics and incorrect conclusions in an article. The article, which was concerned with statistics, mentioned that there were three men who were under observation. One was observed to have imbibed only whiskey and water; the second was observed to have imbibed only bourbon and water; and the third was observed to have drunk only vodka and water. After having drunk these three liquids, it was observed that all three men behaved in a drunken fashion. The one thing that all three men had in common was water. So it was "obvious" that this common denominator, water, must have been that which caused the men to be drunk. (It's not really very difficult to stray pretty far from a reasonable and valid conclusion.)

At one time, it was thought that there were certain preferential origins for people who had multiple sclerosis. It was thought that people from the equatorial latitudes rarely

*This chapter is based partly on information obtained from the Fall '67 issue of *Keynotes,* a publication of the National MS Society.

contracted MS and that people from the northern latitudes were far more susceptible to MS. To the best of my knowledge, this has long since been found to be utterly untrue.

The Scandanavian countries keep remarkably good records of the illnesses of all their inhabitants. In going over these records, someone has pointed out that MS patients rarely come from seacoast towns. It is much more frequent that they come from the mountainous interior sections of the country. This fact has given rise to one of the currently popular ideas of the mechanism by which MS establishes itself. Seafood comprises a much higher fraction of the daily food intake of people who live near the seashore than it does of those who live in the mountainous interior. The seafood, in turn, is known to be rich in polyunsaturated fats. So the current notion states that a diet rich in polyunsaturated fats (as one would get from a diet rich in seafood) may offer some protection from the occurrence of MS. To the best of my knowledge, there is nothing known about the efficacy of seafood after MS has become established. (There is an outside chance, and a completely unverified one, that a diet rich in seafood may help to reduce the severity of subsequent exacerbations after MS has gotten a start). The statistical surveys made in Scandanavia show further that MS patients have a noticeably higher IQ than the average population. The typical MS patient comes from a decidedly higher socio-economic group. The typical MS patient is a white collar worker. The typical MS patient has had a decidedly superior education. (In the latter part of the nineteenth century, the gout was known as the "rich man's disease." It is possible from these studies, that one day MS will be known as the "intelligent man's disease.")

I have heard, from several different doctors, that MS patients as a class know far more about their own disease than do people afflicted with other diseases. This latter condition may be a result of the fact that MS patients are statistically well educated, or it may be due to the fact that MS normally establishes itself at a slow enough rate so that the person can read about the disease before he becomes disabled.

5

Modifications for MS Patients

POSSIBILITIES OF VARIATION OF USE

MY case of MS has affected my hands (among other things) so that I am unable to hold a book while lying down in bed. Since it is occasionally my lot to be confined in bed for weeks at a time, my family and I thought it would be a good idea to try to find some method whereby I could spend my time profitably in reading. (When I sit in my wheelchair, I can easily read a book by simply placing it on a table.) To alleviate the difficulties of reading in bed, I obtained a pair of "prism glasses." I then had a friend construct for me a wooden frame on which was mounted a wire bookholder; in this way, I could be lying flat on my back and the book then would be opened and sitting in this fashion near my chest. If I put the prism glasses on, I can see anything on my chest by simply looking up at the ceiling. It is thus apparent that it is convenient to read books. However this device is practical only when I am confined to bed. Since I am not normally thus confined, it looked offhand as if these special glasses were going to get very little use.

On occasion, I do like to watch TV, and it is not practical

for me to pop out of bed into the wheelchair whenever I want to watch a show. It occurred to me that it might be practical to try wearing these glasses so that I could watch the TV set at its normal position at the foot of my bed. We tried this scheme, and it worked wonderfully! It now makes no difference to me whether I want to watch TV from the wheelchair or lying down in bed. (This is not the original intent of these prism glasses, but I am sure the manufacturer would not object to this additional subuse.)

THINGS TO MAKE AND THINGS TO DO

Let me start off chronologically with the first thing I had made. It was the so-called "johnny seat." Around 1963, when it became apparent that I was having great difficulty standing on my own two feet, it also became apparent that I would have to find some new, convenient method of going to the "john." Since I could stand with help, in front of the dresser, it would then be a relatively simple matter to transfer me to another chair. It could be a seat constructed in the following fashion. It would be welded of ½-inch diameter iron pipe. It would have a wheel at each corner so that it could be easily moved. It would have a toilet seat mounted on it, and this seat would be about 1-inch higher than the regular john in the bathroom. The procedure would be then that I could be seated on this johnny seat and then wheeled into the bathroom to a position directly over the john.

A friend of mine was just as interested as I was in seeing whether or not this scheme would work. I invested $17 in pipes, casters and a toilet seat. The friend of mine assembled it during 1965, and I have used the device ever since. (See Figure 1.) It has worked so very well that I wondered why it wasn't more widely used, perhaps even stocked by distributors of therapeutic furniture. My curiosity was jarred to a

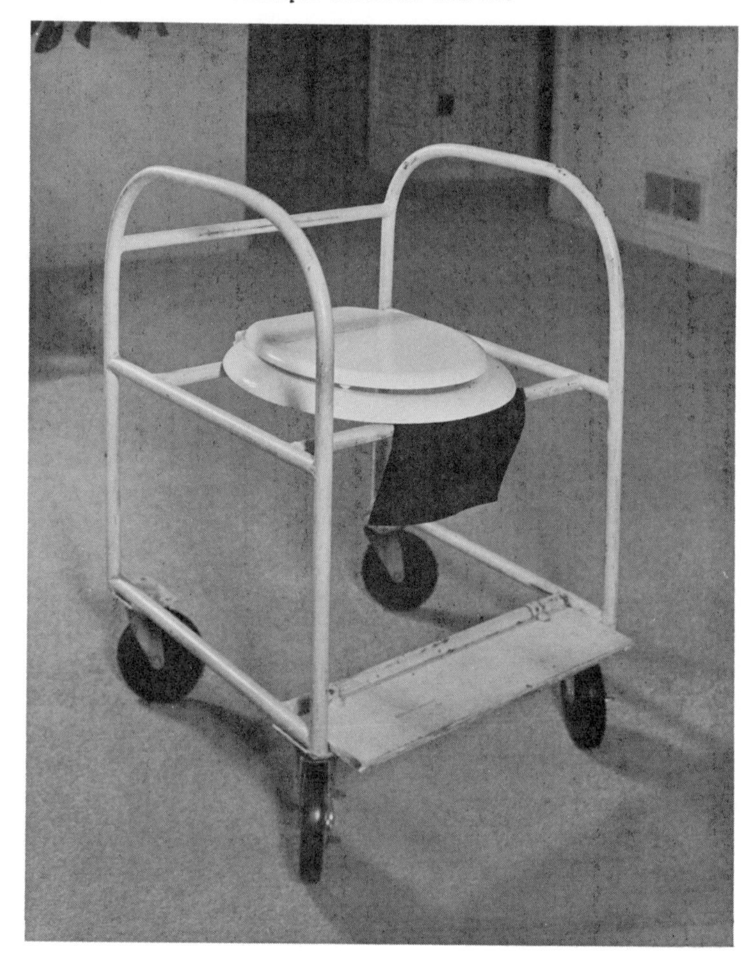

Figure 1. Johnny stool.

halt when I discovered that a virtual "Chinese copy" of my device was made and sold for $153 by one of the distributors of therapeutic furniture.

I think it was my resounding success with the johnny stool that made me think about other simple solutions for problems that people with physical limitations might have. I had been confined to a wheelchair for several years and in that time had discovered that the standard, "garden variety" wheelchair had a small piece of sheet metal hidden under the foot pedal, the purpose of which was to prevent the foot pedal from moving too easily about the iron bar support. When the wheelchair was new, this little piece of metal worked fine. The foot pedal would turn on its iron bar only when a force to turn it was applied. In other words, the foot pedals did not "flop" aimlessly up and down. But if that little piece of metal were ever removed, it seemed to require some sort of a major act of Congress to get it back into position. My personal experience was that once it came out, Buster, there was nothing you could do to get it back where it should be.

Faced with this problem, my mind (which, I hope, is fertile) began to think of all kinds of ways of offering a little bit of friction to the turning of these foot pedals. It occurred to me that I could get hold of one of these small "worm-tightening" hose clamps that are available in any hardware store. This hose clamp could be put on the pipe in such a position that if the foot pedal were to turn, the hose clamp would have to turn, too. Also, since the hose clamp could be tightened or loosened, it would be possible to require more or less force to turn the foot pedals. I obtained two of these hose clamps, at 21¢ apiece and asked a friend of mine to install them. (Installation takes 21 seconds – perhaps 23 seconds for a person who has never done it before.) The assembly is shown in Figure 2. This second

Figure 2. Modification to wheelchair.

operation was, again, such a capital success that I am almost driven to the point of thinking of myself as an innovator.

Of course, one of the big difficulties with MS is that one's physical abilities may vary enormously from day to day. Because of this tremendous variation, a mechanical aid which is workable one day may be of no use at all another day. This extensive variability is another one of the things which make misunderstandings likely. (Please refer to Chapter 6 on misunderstandings.)

I am at present trying to devise something that will help me practice standing up. (When I explain that I am reputed to have an "unusual obsession with standing up," perhaps this will be offered as additional proof.) The point is that by continuing to do what one can, by using devices to help one do that which one can almost do by oneself, one can ensure that at least groups of his muscles still work. This is a wonderful introduction to a word of advice I would like to give to other MS patients, which is in the form of an entreaty. The advice is: By gosh, if there is any particular thing that you can do now, please, by all means, keep on doing it. If necessary, keep on practicing it to make sure that it doesn't simply slip away, because it is certain that once you have stopped doing something for several months, your ability to do it again simply disappears, and this disappearance is, unfortunately, an irreversible process. A person with most of his normal faculties can normally practice these things that happen to be lost. However the process is so marginal in the case of MS patients, that once lost, these abilities are virtually impossible to regain. I cannot urge other MS patients too strongly not to give up any normal practices. The idea of training new muscles to do new tasks is appealing from a scientific point of view, but hardly so from a patient's point of view. I am convinced that much remains to be learned about the cause and cure of MS, but I am also convinced that much could be done to alleviate this situation in MS by the proper and sensible application of physical therapy.

After my obvious success with the johnny seat, I became convinced more than ever that it made good sense for a person with MS to think of modifications that would allow him to do things which would be perfectly ordinary for a person without MS. In the succeeding years, opportunities have presented themselves to make modifications for certain purposes. None of these has been so obviously successful as the johnny stool, but perhaps some reader can get an idea from their descriptions. It is with this hope in mind that I mention some of the modifications that I have made and tried.

One day, I happened to pull a muscle in my leg, so that although I was normally able to stand and lock my knees, the pulled muscle prevented me from doing this. If the pulled muscle took a long time in repairing itself, I was afraid that I might lose the ability to stand and "lock" my knees completely. I happened to be in the hospital a few weeks later, and I was aware of the fact that they had a "tilt table" down in the physical therapy department. A tilt table is in essence a plywood table which can be raised from a horizontal position to a vertical position. The patient can be placed on the table while it is horizontal, belts and fasteners can be attached to the proper places, and then the table can be raised to any angle up to and including 90 degrees, or straight up and down. If a belt is placed across the patient's knees, so that his knees cannot possibly buckle, then the patient can be raised to a vertical position. In this position, he will be using all the muscles normally used in the standing position with the obvious exception of those which prevent the knees from buckling. When I had pulled my muscles, I was very anxious to try to use the tilt table in order to be sure to maintain what little ability to stand up that I had.

As I do so often, I began to think of some simple modification so that I might have my own tilt table at home and use it in case I happened to pull that muscle again. The modification I thought of was this: I could buy a flush door from a lumberyard and attach a small perpendicular footrest at the bottom of the door. Then I could obtain some automobile safety seat belts and put them on the door at such places that I could put one belt directly over my kneecap when I was lying down on the door, one across my chest and under the arms, and possibly one across my stomach. Then I could be placed on the flush door, and the belts appropriately fastened, A helper could then raise the head part of the door and lean the top part against the wall. In this way, I could be raised to 80 degrees or so from the horizontal. This is partically straight up and down, and I feel that the additional 10 degrees is hardly worth mentioning. If one insisted on being straight up and down, then the possiblity of falling forward on one's face is too painful to consider.

I have never made such a modified tilt table but I certainly intend to try something of this sort, if it is indicated in my condition. Other ideas which might come under this category are increasingly trivial, but I mention them just in case they may answer a long-felt need for some MS patients.

I have, at home, a device known as a "hoyer" or patient lifter. This is essentially a device operated by a hydraulic jack, which can be used to lift the patient to move him from here to there. We use the device to transfer me from the wheelchair to the bed; from a wheelchair into the front seat of an automobile; from a wheelchair onto my johnny stool. The hoyer operates very well and without difficulty with one small exception. That exception, which is trivial except when it makes the hoyer unusable, is the sleeve around each of the pins. Each sleeve is a piece of sheet copper bent into the form of a 3/8-inch o.d. sleeve. After many usings, this sleeve can work its way out and fall to the ground. To prevent such a loss, I have inserted a threaded screw through the sleeve, with a large washer at the head end and another one at the nut end. Such a retainer can easily be affixed to prevent the loss of the sleeve.

Once, a few years ago, when I was no longer able to walk well, I happened to be home alone in my wheelchair. Then, the most embarrassing of all things happened; I fell out of my wheelchair. (Please don't ask me to tell you how one can fall out of a wheelchair. It sounds impossible to me too, but I guarantee you, it happened.) Since that unfortunate occurrence, I have had an opportunity to think of how I might possibly have fallen out of the wheelchair. It might have happened in this way: Assume that one's bottom moved forward in the wheelchair a little bit. The natural tendency, then, is to try to sit up straight by grasping the front of the wheelchair. But when one pulls this way, there is a possibility (especially if things are not going your way) that you will simply succeed in pulling your bottom still more forward. If this is done a few times, it is very easy to pull one's bottom off the wheelchair seat, at which time gravity then takes over and deposits you (sometimes not too gently) on the floor. So, on this day, there I was, flat on my back on the floor. I was fortunate, however, that I avoided striking my head on parts of the wheelchair.

The situation was this: I was flat on my back on the floor. I couldn't get up. No one was scheduled to come visit us for several hours. My wife was out and would not be home for several hours. I wasn't in any pain, but it was dreadfully boring to be simply lying there on the floor with nothing to do. I happened to be on a smooth linoleum floor and by wiggling my arms, I was able to pull myself over to my desk, where the telephone was. From my low vantage point at the side of the desk, I was able to see that there were three cords going up to the surface of the desk. One of them went to the telephone, one to my dictaphone machine, and the third to the speaker phone. I chose one and pulled. (One isn't normally happy to be hit in the head, but I assure you, I was overjoyed that day when the telephone came bouncing down off the desk and hit me.)

When I got the telephone, I rang for the operator and asked if I could be connected with the police department. When I reached the police department, I had to try to explain, "You'll never believe this, but I am flat on my back. I wonder if you can send two people over to help put me back in my wheelchair." I suspect that the police are used to stories that are even weirder than that. After a few minutes, the police came and I could hear their car pull into the driveway. Then I realized that this might be a very unpleasant procedure indeed. We happen to have a dog, and like many dogs, he thinks of himself as sole owner of all he can survey. Anybody who dares to come on our property is obviously a trespasser and the dog, accordingly, acts as ferociously as possible in order to scare these people off "his" land.

I usually call our dog by the nickname "Stoopie," although his given name is Hi-Fi. (This nickname I have chosen is not intended to reflect on the dog's intellectual achievements, nor on his posture.) The situation at the moment was that I was flat on my back, relatively immobile; the police had pulled into our driveway and were in the garage about to come into the den. The dog was snarling like a wild beast in anticipation of some fresh, live meat "on the hoof." Apparently the police didn't realize what a wild, savage-sounding beast he was, because they fearlessly opened the den door and simply walked right in. At that moment, Hi-Fi showed his true colors; he turned and ran (faster than I have ever seen him go) to the other end of the house as soon as he caught sight of the "Blue Coats." (My own personal explanation of this fact is that Hi-Fi had probably, some time before, committed some sort of a misdemeanor and simply didn't want to get mixed up with the police again.)

The point of the whole story is that having fallen out of my wheelchair once, I was not anxious to have the same thing happen again. So I bought an automobile safety seat belt. I conned my brother into attaching the thing to my wheelchair. For a while there, I had one of the few wheelchairs fixed up with a safety belt. It was a wonderful conversation piece. I used to point out that the fellow who dresses me in the morning is one of the few people at Princeton Hospital who has gotten a summons for exceeding the speed limit in a wheelchair. (A ridiculous picture just popped into my mind. Wouldn't it be something if speed limit signs were posted on the walls of a hospital?)

As I became more and more dependent on the wheelchair, it became more and more apparent that it would be a good idea to construct a ramp so that the wheelchair, with me as passenger, could be taken outside. To solve this problem, I built such a ramp which goes from the floor level of the den in our house, down to the floor level of the garage. The ramp is made of ¾-inch plywood and is reinforced by two pieces of 2-inch by 3-inch lumber. I think that people in the "building game" may regard this as a ridiculous amount of overprotection, but I feel that the few additional pennies spent for wood, nails, etcetera, are a very cheap form of insurance. (I may be a pauper, but at least I'll be a live pauper.)

The next problem that I tried to solve concerns the problem of nighttime sleep. There are two effects which I think are common among MS patients and which this description seems to solve satisfactorily. First, there is the characteristic known as urinary urgency; that is, when one has to urinate, one really has to. When the signal comes to urinate, one can't hold it back. In addition to this urinary urgency, I have the difficulty that if my knee gets bent, by a spasmodic reflex for example, I have great difficulty in straightening it back out again. Both of these problems are completely solved in my case by the following stratagem.

When I am put to bed to go to sleep, I have a plywood board (which is about ½-inch thick, about 24 inches wide, and about 4 feet long) which is placed under my legs. It extends from approximately the bottom of my buttocks to a few inches past my heels. Then an ordinary glass urinal is put in place between my legs. To hold the urinal in place all night, I have a piece of wood shaped like an L with a long stem and a short base. This piece of wood is shown in the accompanying photograph (Fig. 3). The foot of the L is placed up against the bottom of the glass urinal, and a C-clamp holds the upright of the L to the sheet of plywood. Then a 2-inch wide cloth belt, purchased at an Army-Navy surplus store, is belted so as to hold my knees down close to the sheet of plywood. The net effect is that the urinal is held in place all night long, and I can't possibly bend my knees, even accidentally, to dislodge it.

Before this stratagem was adopted, I used to accidentally douse myself every few weeks or so. I have used this device for about three years now and am happy to report that only once in all that time have I had an accident. (Even in that case, the accident was due to an obviously improperly-placed urinal.) I would earnestly recommend this device for people who are incontinent, even though they may not have MS. The main consideration is whether or not they would be willing to trade the possible irritation and possibility of infection for the lack of mobility implied by the belt.

I happen to be fairly fond of reading, and one of the difficulties that I have is that my fingers have neither the

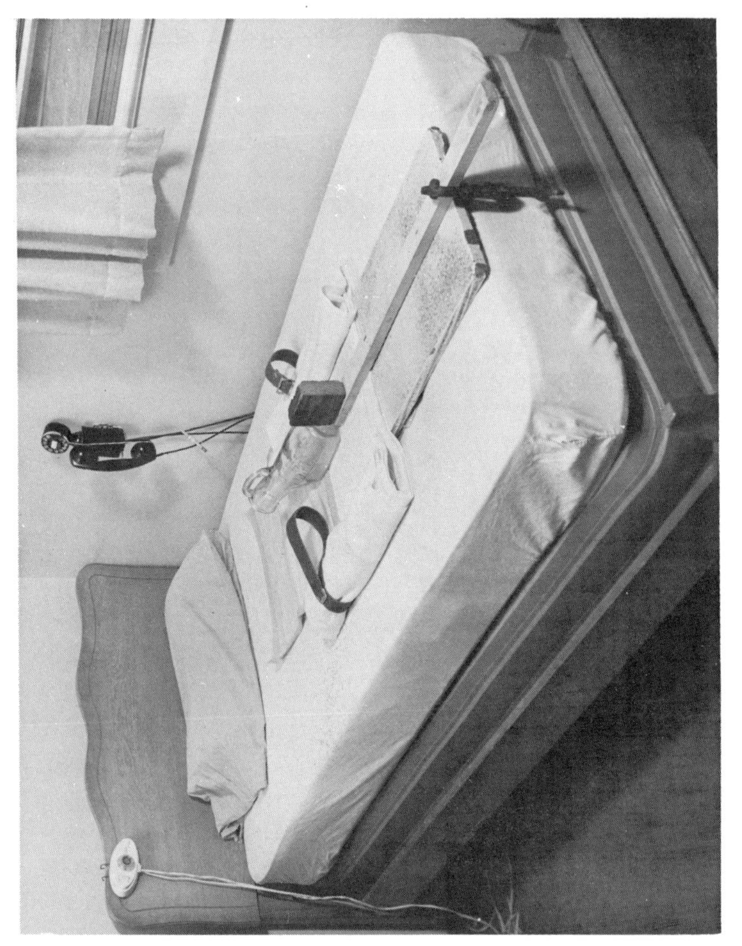

Figure 3. Nighttime anti-soaking device.

strength nor dexterity required to turn a page. In order to get around this problem, the page-turner shown in Figures 4a and 4b has been developed. (I have called this device a page-turner for patients with mutiple sclerosis and GOKHMOs.*) Since my head and neck muscles are virtually unaffected, I decided to make a page-turner which could be grasped between the teeth and which would have an eraser at the other end to provide some friction. My brother-in-law, who happens to be a dentist, was kind enough to make the entire device for me.

The wooden extension has a 1-inch length of 1/8-inch diameter dowel stock at the upper end in order to anchor it firmly in the dental impression material. The eraser at the lower end of the device does not get used as an eraser and therefore never wears out.

The holder for the page-turner looks almost like a piece of modern art; but when the page-turner is used, no part of the holder is found to be useless.

The pages of some books are more difficult to turn than the pages of others, but this is so even for those who don't have MS. Also, the pages of some books tend to flip back closed. In order to get around this, I have discovered that my left hand serves as a wholly admirable paperweight to keep these books open to the right place. I have also found that this page-turner can be used with magazines and newspapers as well as with books.

The one item that appears to be almost extraneous is the little piece of blotter which is held horizontally under the mouthpiece. This entire device was an afterthought; when I first used the page-turner, I was annoyed to discover that the mouthpiece frequently collects saliva and this saliva then drips from the mouthpiece onto the table. In order to preclude this messy situation, I arranged the horizontal piece of blotting paper so that it would catch the drops of saliva.

*God Only Knows How Many Others.

Figure 4a. The page-turner.

Figure 4b. The page-turner in action.

6

Misunderstandings

MISUNDERSTANDINGS between people who have MS and others who do not are, unfortunately, common. The reasons for the occurrence and high incidence of these misunderstandings can be general and diffuse. For example, in one case, the patient with MS is in a wheelchair and "claims" not to be able to pick up a glass. I put that word "claims" in quotation marks because I am sure that many people, upon seeing a seemingly normal person, will find it inconceivable that he cannot pick up a glass. Yet, this is precisely the case. The person in the wheelchair may not be able to stretch his arms out far enough to reach the glass, or he may be able to stretch it out far enough to reach the glass but his fingers cannot be controlled so that he can pick the glass up.

Another possibility is that the patient was known from the time long before he had MS, and it is difficult to associate the present inability with the previously able person. In either of these cases, it requires great understanding to recognize all the limitations.

Sometimes these misunderstandings can be very serious in nature; sometimes they are mostly comical in nature; and sometimes they are combinations of the two.

I shall never forget the time that I was in a medical

hospital and spoke to a social worker. Her job was primarily to see if she could smooth over any rough spots that might exist between the patient and his family. To gather her facts, she interviewed me one morning, and one of the questions she asked was, "What do you want, more than anything in the world, that we should be able to do for you at the hospital?" I quickly dismissed all answers having to do with sexual prowess and finally answered, "I suppose I would like, more than anything else, to be able to walk again." I didn't sneak a look into the social worker's notebook, but I am sure she must have written something like, "M-m-m-m, patient seems to have unnatural obsession with walking." I became aware of this because my wife accidentally said to me one day, "But this unnatural obsession of yours with walking. . ." Even my doctor was taken in by this expression. He spoke to my wife several time about this "unnatural obsession with walking."

Now I will be the first to agree that obsessions of any kind whatsoever should be curbed, but I also believe that the question that the social worker asked me at the hospital was a loaded one. The answer to that question would have to be very carefully evaluated, and it may be meaningful only when given in conjunction with other questions. All in all, I feel that the social worker asked a very inexpert question, and she interpreted it in a very inexpert fashion.

Unfortunately, misunderstandings can be far more common than simply the ones between MS patients and hospital personnel. The cases where it hurts the most are when it occurs between the MS patient and a member of his family; this is simply because his contact with hospital personnel is of a transitory nature, whereas his contact with his family is constant.

I suppose my reputation for having an "unnatural obsession with walking" got an additional nudge when I happened to be at a different hospital and told my wife about a conversation I had had with the physical therapist there. In my conversation with the therapist, I had asked if there are any advantages which I would get if I could arrange some means of standing for several minutes a day. He said, "If you could arrange to stand for several minutes a day, there are many, many advantages which would benefit you. For example, you will find that all your bodily elimination processes would work much better. You would also find that you would feel better generally."

Today I am able to lock my knees and to stand in an upright position, if somebody will stand by to make sure I don't fall, for ten, perhaps even fifteen, seconds at a time. It seemed to me that this was a wonderful basis to start from. I might be able to stand only ten seconds at a time for the first week, but then it could gradually be built up and then I could stand for perhaps fifteen, then twenty, then twenty-five, then – who knows? Perhaps even a minute at a time, eventually. But when I mentioned my desire to build some sort of means to help me stand up, I was again plagued with the phrase, "an unnatural obsession with walking."

It is apparent that a great deal is not known about the disease MS. But it seems to me that it is completely incorrect to equate the thoughts "not much is known about the cause of MS" and "nothing will do any good to help alleviate the difficulties of people who have MS."

It is very unfortunate that simple, verbal exchanges, which were intended as very low-level comments, can turn out to be bristling with inuendos as in the following case:

> The husband comes downstairs and says, "Good morning, dear."
> And the wife wheels around swiftly and says, "What did you mean by that remark? Why are you always jumping at me, Harry?"

One may also find that the language which was perfectly suitable while one was well, may not be suitable after MS has struck. It is unfortunate, but true, that MS does not confer an ability at clairvoyance to its victims. So, when the patient, who cannot reach a book in the middle of the table asks, "May I please have that book over there?" the answer may very well be a snappy "Can't you see that I am just about to give it to you?" or an even more annoyed, "Do you need it right now?" A defense on the patient's part which says, "But I didn't ask for it right now" will be of no avail. The seeds of a misunderstanding are already sown and it is a very touchy question to try to decide which way the plant will lean.

7

Beneficial Effects of Therapy

I SUSPECT that some reader may carelessly glance at the titles of these various chapters and come to the conclusion that this must be a very thorough book. But as I have mentioned before, I am writing only about my own personal observations and my own personal experiences. I do not guarantee, therefore, that all observations are medically sound. My impression is that physical therapy can be divided into two kinds: active therapy and passive therapy. Active therapy is that in which the patient himself does the work. Passive therapy, on the other hand, is performed by therapists on the patient. The point of therapy, active or passive, is to see to it that those groups of muscles which are not being used constantly do not wither away and atrophy. My own personal list of therapeutic exercises can undoubtedly be improved by any competent therapist; I merely mention it in order to make the history somewhat complete.

I have a set of weights which can be attached to the wall and which can be raised by pulling on a handle which is attached by a rope to the weights. From my wheelchair, I can pull on these handles and presumably thus exercise some of my arm muscles. I normally do each exercise only four or five times, so that I never get "pooped." After this wall exercise, I get pushed in the wheelchair over to the bed, where I can be transferred to a sitting position at the side of the bed. This transfer is accomplished by a friend standing me up from the wheelchair (Boy! What an obsession with walking!) and then letting me sit down at the edge of the bed. From this sitting position, one tries gently to push me back over. I try to resist this pushing-over and thus try to strengthen my stomach muscles. After this stomach-strengthening exercise, I lie down on my back. My friend can offer me some slight resistance and I try to bend my arms from an outstretched position over to my shoulders. Then he pushes down on my forehead while I try to lift my head. Suddenly, he lets go. I think that this also strengthens the stomach muscles. After this, we start exercising on the legs. He lifts each leg in turn to a perfectly straight position, with the knees straight. After this, he twists my foot as if I were trying to twist the foot above the ankle. After this, he takes the "pole" which is actually a broomstick and holds it directly in front of me, I grab it and try to pull down on the pole, going through the same motion that I used to go through in "chinning." Then I change my position on the broomstick handle and try pushing up against a slight resistance from my friend.

When this is all finished, I get turned over on my stomach. On my stomach, my leg is first bent at the knee. Then, holding my leg straight, it is picked up from the hip. After this, my fingers get pulled and pushed to see that they don't get stiff and immobile. When all these things have been done, we are ready for the "grand finale." This "grand finale" consists of five (count them 1 – 2 – 3 – 4 – 5) lady push-ups. (A lady push-up has been defined for me as one which is a push-up from the knees on up.)

The course of MS is so erratic that sometimes I am unable

to do a single push-up of this sort and then later in the week, I am able to do five in a row. On an average night, I may be able to do two or three in a row but then will have to rest before doing the remaining three or two.

The whole point of therapy is to try to enable you to keep doing that which you can now do. It is surprising how easy it is to lose the ability to do any particular thing. I add an earnest entreaty to all MS patients: Please don't give up anything without at least a "good old try."

8

Possible Effects of the Weather

MS appears in so many different forms and different people are so differently affected that it is very difficult to make any statement that applies equally well to all MS patients.

The effects of weather on MS patients are as varied as are the effects of weather on the rest of the population who do not have MS – only more so. The effects of varying air pressure, varying humidity and so forth, are known to exist, but they are not consistent from one person to another.

It has been known for years that the behavior of groups of animals is very dependent on changing weather conditions. Cows, for example, are said to become very sullen before an approaching storm. But apparently, none of these effects on animals has been sufficiently consistent to be used as a weather predictor. There has recently been an attempt to show that the concentration of positive or negative ions in the air can have a great effect on the behavior of animals and human beings. Some of these experiments have gone so far as to suggest that human burn patients can be greatly helped by exposure to air which has a concentration of positive ions in it. Many experiments on the effects of ionization in the air have been performed by Dr. C. W. Hansell at the RCA Laboratories. Because of the presumably beneficial effects of ionization, some companies have been making small, portable air ionizers for use in the home. Dr. Hansell collected a great many reports of the beneficial effects resulting from air ionization, and he published these in a lengthy technical report for RCA.

Perhaps one of the most curious things that he talks about is the story in the Bible concerning the time that Moses saw the burning bush. The Bible tells us that the bush was completely enveloped in flames, and yet the bush was not consumed. Dr. Hansell thinks that this was probably a natural atmospheric effect which could be explained by ionization. The chances that atmospheric ionization did, indeed, play a part in this phenomenon are not at all remote when we consider the existence of St. Elmo's fire, which is a well-known effect occurring on sailing vessels and which is due to atmospheric ionization. In this case, the tops of the masts of sailing vessels are often seen to be enveloped in fire, but the fire is not real; it might be termed an optical illusion due to atmospheric electricity and ionization.

I was particularly fascinated by Dr. Hansell's report because one of the items in it was a report of the beneficial effect to a multiple sclerosis patient. When I became aware of these possibly beneficial effects, I became very anxious to try out the ionizer. I borrowed an air ionizer (it was a very small piece of apparatus) and placed it near my bed. For the first week, I was constantly bathed in positive ions; and for the second week, I was constantly bathed in negative ions. I am sorry to have to report that I could observe no change whatsoever in my physical condition.

The effects of ionization in other areas of medicine are said to be a bit more consistent. Some years ago, a hospital in

Philadelphia equipped one of its hospital rooms with an air ionizer. The room was reserved exclusively for patients with extensive skin burns. It was thought that the presence of ionization could promote the healing of the skin injuries; would reduce the pain associated with the burns; and had other beneficial qualities. From the fact that the results of this experiment were not widely circulated and that the "ionization process" has not become a standard method of treatment, I surmise that the results of that first experiment were not conclusive.

As far as the effects of atmospheric disturbances on my own physical condition, I can honestly say that during the period before a rain, I invariably feel the adverse effect; this happens in EVERY SINGLE CASE, with the possible exception of all those cases when I feel better before a rain. Since the effect of atmospheric conditions upon my physical condition are so very definite, I have decided to try to put these to a scientific use. There was only one small problem remaining: How do I determine whether it WILL or WILL NOT RAIN? But as soon as this small difficulty is ironed out, I am ready to go into the business of weather prediction.

9

A Typical Day

IT is my purpose, in this chapter, to describe my activities on a typical day – not because I think that they are of supreme interest, but because other people might be curious to know how at least one MS patient spends his day.

I happen to be fortunate in that I have obtained the services of a young man who works at the local hospital. On the average weekday, he stops at our house before he goes to work. He dresses me and gets me "set up for business" in a matter of twenty minutes or so. The net result is that I am ready to go to "work" every morning at about 8 o'clock. My "work" fits into a category rather different from the usual "work."

On this "average day," I normally have breakfast at around 8:00. After breakfast, I am wheeled into our den, and there I sit at my desk. My activities at the desk consist primarily of reading something or other. I have more scientific-type journals on my desk than I would care to shake a stick at, and I try, but not very successfully, to read these journals. Unfortunately, the pile keeps growing week by week, and I confess I don't know what the final result will be, but it sure is fun trying to keep up with the magazines.

Not only do I read at the desk, I also do my dictating there. I can dictate personal letters, business letters, book manuscripts and any other manuscripts I choose on this machine. I usually try to restrict my reading and dictating to the morning. I save the afternoon for the newspaper, but I can easily be convinced to do some dictating in the afternoon.

After a day spent at the desk reading and dictating, I am as ready as anybody else for a good supper. (That's one thing I can be thankful for – I don't have any lack of appetite.) After supper, there is normally a half-hour gap of unfilled time before my next scheduled activity starts. The next thing I do is a bit of physical therapy.

Having had physical therapy performed on me by quite a few different therapists, I felt that nearly the same benefits could be achieved by engaging the services of a person whose prime qualifications are a modest intelligence and a few muscles. Such a man could go through the routine approximating as closely as possible the same procedures that physical therapists did. I have had three or four people to do such therapy for me. (The reasons that the two or three quit is completely disassociated from me, my family or my condition.) On several occasions, professional physical therapists happened to be visiting at our house, and I verbally outlined the routine that I was following for the physical therapy. In each case, they agreed that my program was a reasonable and satisfactory one.

After half an hour or so of physical therapy, I am ready for bed. (Not because I am tired or sleepy, but rather because it is easier for the therapist to put me directly in bed, rather than put me in a wheelchair and then have my wife get me from the wheelchair to the bed.) I try not to let those hours before sleep be utterly wasted hours. For example, I am fond, on occasion, of writing something or other. The hours before "lights out" can be very profitably spent reviewing phrases and construction. Another one of my many little side activities is that I write a mathematical problem column for the newsletter of a local technical organization (the Princeton section of the IEEE). During those few hours between the time I am put in bed and the time I fall asleep, I can exercise my mind by trying to think of suitable problems for the next month's issue or by trying to solve some of the old problems mentally. (As the phrase goes, "if you haven't tried it, don't knock it.")

My thoughts during the evening are not always confined to these subjects. I sometimes allow my mind to wander in a perfectly free fashion to whatever subject is most pleasant. I confess that these hours spent thinking in a completely undisciplined manner are among the most enjoyable.

The activities that I have described thus far are those associated with a perfectly normal weekday. On weekends, of course, we slip into a different routine. The biggest and most obvious change from the weekday is the existence of the Sunday *New York Times* as opposed to the daily *New York Times.* I have heard so many people complain that they don't get a chance to read the entire Sunday *New York Times.* All I can say is, if a perfectly normal person can't read it all, what chance do you suppose a guy who has difficulty turning pages will have? But one advantage of having to go through the *Times* at a slower pace is that one can devote one's full attention to the "cream" of the *Times.*

Weekends are also a good time to have company. If we happen to have company, I feel sure that the only reason they would have for suspecting that I might not be completely normal is that I happen to be sitting in a wheelchair.

Every few weeks, or so, I take a trip into the RCA-Astro Electronics Division; as I mentioned before I used to work at RCA before I became disabled. My trips now-adays are completely unofficial – they are almost entirely social in nature. I see the fellows I used to work with and enjoy talking things over with them.

Another activity which takes place primarily on weekends is that of visiting friends. The only restrictions on such visits is that there be somebody around to help me get from the automobile to the wheelchair. (This restriction hardly ever prevents me from going some place.) My occasional trips into RCA are surely beneficial from my point of view. It is very kind of RCA to allow me to come in for such obviously "unofficial" visits, but my activities while there are consistent with the notion that RCA is a commercial enterprise and that AED was not set up to play games.

At this point, I would like to digress slightly and describe my activities on a very untypical day. The particular untypical days that I have in mind are the days spent on our vacation in Hawaii. In 1967, we decided that inasmuch as we (both my wife and I) were not getting any younger, it was "now or never" if we were ever going to get to the island of Hawaii. So we decided to go with my brother-in-law and my sister-in-law. I had heard stories about how the air-lines bend over backward in order to make flying tolerable for incapacitated people such as myself. Because of this, I trusted them, and I have found since that my trust was not misplaced. Many of the facts concerning our trip seem to fit into this chapter. To begin with, we had planned our trip on the only airline which does not involve a change of planes in San Francisco.

When we got to the airport in New York, I was transferred, at the airline's request, from my own wheelchair into the airline's special wheelchair. Their special wheelchair was about three inches narrower than my own. The reason for this was simply so that the wheelchair could travel down the aisle of the plane a little bit easier. This sounded like a very reasonable thing, and I began to be very favorably impressed by the airlines. Eventually, the time for boarding the plane came. I was wheeled down a canopy-type platform, directly into the passenger compartment of the plane. We entered in the front part of the plane, and our seats were directly behind the first-class section. As we started to go down the aisle in the first-class section, the wheelchair fit very comfortably. However the aisle is tapered and gets narrower toward the tail of the plane, but I had confidence that since I was in a specially designed wheelchair, there would be no difficulty in traversing the entire length of the aisle. Or so one would think. But, you guessed it! The wheelchair could get no more than half-way down the length of the aisle. Fortunately, I happened to have a good, strong brother-in-law along with me. He was able to pick me up and carry me back to the tourist section of the plane. I have since wondered what the airlines would have done if I had not had such a strong brother-in-law with me. It is difficult for me to picture a group of stewardesses carrying an immobilized passenger. Maybe they get training in this sort of thing, but I still wonder. If the airlines went to the trouble of designing and buying a special wheelchair which was a bit narrower than the standard wheelchair, would it not have been expected that this special wheelchair could go down the entire length of the aisle? I confess to being very confused about this point. Once in my seat, however, my behavior was no different than that of any other passenger.

When we got to Hawaii, they had a special lifting platform which could be used to raise or lower the wheelchair from the plane entrance to ground level. At the airport, I could again be transferred into a different one of their wheelchairs. Again, the services of a good, strong brother-in-law can be used to get one from the wheelchair into a cab. At the hotel, the transfer from cab to wheelchair can again be easily made if one has a strong brother-in-law.

Once at the hotel, all the arrangements which we had made by mail appeared to work like clockwork. We had written to the MS Society of Hawaii to ask if we could make arrangements to rent a patient-lifter, a johnny stool and to see if we could engage a local physical therapist while we were in Hawaii. After we got there, we discovered that things in Hawaii are very much like they are in any large American city. We were able to rent a patient-lifter,* we were able to rent a johnny seat, and we were able to find a physical therapist. All in all, the difficulties associated with MS appeared to be as much under control on the island of Hawaii as they would be anywhere in the United States.

My activities on the island of Hawaii did not differ much from my activities at home. In the morning, breakfast was not unusual. A day spent at the beach under a large umbrella was not unusual. Again, the evenings were not unusual except in the sense that they were so very pleasant and beautiful.

I did not feel particularly full of pep, energy, vim and vigor while I was in Hawaii, but neither did I feel enervated. In other words, I can report no observable beneficial effects from simply living in Hawaii, but it sure wasn't detrimental either!

While I was on the beach in Hawaii, my eyeballs got lots of exercise looking at the lissome lasses clad in bikini bathing suits. I am sure this exercise is beneficial to all males and I recommend it heartily to all, especially the MS patients.

Our trip back from the island of Hawaii to New York was almost a rerun of the trip from New York to Hawaii, with one small exception. We stopped in San Francisco for about an hour on the return trip. During this stop, everybody got out of the plane to "stretch their legs," with the obvious exception of "yours truly." But I didn't mind sitting on the

*We have one of these hoyer-type patient-lifters at home, thanks to a long-term arrangement with the Multiple Sclerosis Service Organization.

plane. While I was sitting there, the stewardess came through, tidying up the plane, and suddenly, she saw me – an apparently normal individual. She somehow became convinced that I was a stowaway. I spent a most pleasant fifteen minutes trying to convince her that I was not.

10

Years 0 to 29

THE present chapter will be concerned with my history up until I was diagnosed as having MS. I do this in the hope that some reader may be able to see similarities and correlate happenings in my story with happenings in the histories of other MS patients.

I haven't checked on the weather record, but I feel sure that the day on which I was born must have been a beautiful, sunny day. The reason for this certainty is simply that so much has happened to me that has been very good. (I feel that the few unfortunate things can be chalked up as "errors" on the part of the Programmer.)

My earliest recollection goes all the way back to a time when I was in my baby carriage. It may be only an imaginary picture that I have of myself in a carriage, but I don't know how one would check that.

When I was four years old, or so, water from the city mains was distasteful, and so my parents used to buy bottled spring water. Once a week or so, a man would come and deliver a case of gallon jugs, each filled with spring water. One day, I (helpful tot that I was) decided to go downstairs and bring up one of these gallon jugs of water. There happened to be a step between our laundry room and the cellar. I went down to the cellar, took the gallon jug of water (which was almost as large as I was) and started to carry it. I forgot all about the step and tripped over it. The bottle fell on the concrete floor, smashed to smithereens and I fell face down on top of it. I got a gash across my cheek which started in the corner of my eye. Since I am now a parent myself, I can understand the feeling my mother must have had when she saw me with the blood gushing from my face. As is so often the case with women, she was the absolute model of calm, cool behavior while the "chips were down." She waited until I was all taken care of at the hospital before she "let go." Another one of my very early recollections is one of my walking down the street with that bandage on my eye. The other little kids gaped at me, probably thinking that I was some sort of a deformed monster.

Shortly after this, I started to go to school. My preparation for school was not extremely detailed but, on the other hand, was undoubtedly adequate. As a child, I spoke the Yiddish language more than English. I had the job of learning the English alphabet and learning how to write English. But in that sense, I was no different than any of the other kids.

I can still remember the fear and terror I felt my first day of school. My mother had taken me to the school in the morning and left me there. The sliding doors between adjacent rooms had been opened, and all the children were in a very large room which was five normal rooms long and one normal room wide. This was all part of the normal morning "assembly" period. When the assembly period was over, the lucky kids who had been chosen to do so closed the sliding doors. I had never seen anything of this sort before in my life, and I became convinced that these "blackguards" were simply trying to separate me and a few other people from the rest of humanity. I was petrified! The prisoner in Edgar Alan Poe's *The Pit and the Pendulum* must have had similar feelings as the walls started to close in on him. The sad forebodings of that first day, however, never did come to pass.

As I look back on those days in elementary school, I can see that they are undoubtedly some of my most carefree and pleasantly spent days. In spite of such harrowing experiences, it is hard for me to think of any extended period of time so free and easy.

At that time, there were what is called the "children's concerts" being performed by the Philadelphia orchestra under the leadership of Leopold Stokowski. My parents bought me a subscription to these "Children's Concerts." (This must have been similar to the present-day theory that "by gosh, these kids are going to get culture, and they're going to enjoy it!") My mother used to come to school a little bit before school let out to pick me up to take me over to the trolley car so that I could go into town to attend these concerts. I could only have been about six years old, and I am not sure that I would be willing to trust an unknown trolley car conductor or motorman with my six-year-old child, but apparently the drive to expose children to "culture" was great enough to minimize the dangers associated with trusting your six-year-old to an unknown trolley car conductor. Somehow, nothing ever happened to me; it all worked out fine. When the concert was over, my father (who worked a mere mile or so away) was waiting for me, and we used to go home together. I was growing up now. I used to come home when all the "big guys" would come for supper.

In elementary school, another incident took place which, thankfully, did not leave any signs of permanent trauma. I had "skipped" the second half of my second year of elementary school. On my first day in the next class, the teacher gave us an exercise sheet on which we were to practice the addition of simple arithmetical fractions. Presumably, a method for doing this had been prescribed the latter half of the second year, but I had been "skipped" and was not familiar with the "approved" method of adding these fractions. But I was not completely stupid! If I had to add 1¼ and 2½, I would picture the appropriate number of pies and simply write down the answer. After we had completed this little test, each student exchanged his paper with someone else in the class and marked it for correctness. My paper showed absolutely no work – only the final answer. According to the "approved" method, this was incorrect because it didn't show any work. The student marking my paper asked the teacher, and the teacher suggested I had undoubtedly copied from someone else because no work was shown. This has, I am sure, happened to many other people, and I earnestly urge all elementary schoolteachers not to attribute the correct answer to cheating or copying in all those cases where the work is not shown.

After elementary school, a perfectly ordinary intermediate school followed – ordinary except that our family moved in the middle of this school year to the other side of the city. This move had a most fortunate consequence for me. We moved to the same block on which lived the girl who was to become my wife.

Toward the end of our intermediate schooling, the students were required to choose an appropriate subject for study in high school. Of course, we had discussions and assignments concerning this choice. Since my father was a jeweler, I assumed that I, also, would become a jeweler. I began to make my plans accordingly. But in the midst of these preparations, I discovered that most of my friends were going to take the "academic" course. The academic course was a preparation for college, and I couldn't see much point in taking a course to prepare me to go some place where I probably couldn't go. Going to college was such a financial burden that there was no question in my mind but that I couldn't go. But I was young at the time and the thought of being separated from my friends, because of their taking an academic course and my taking an "industrial" course, was also unthinkable. So, out of sheer loyalty to my friends (and what I privately thought was a vain pursuit), I signed up for the academic course. I don't think I need point out how glad I am now that I took this academic course. From the very day I entered high school, I had a ball.

The days spent in high school were the most delightful I can remember. I made many friendships there, good and lasting friendships. I graduated from high school in 1939. As graduation day drew near, one of my friends suggested, "Say, look. We've been good friends all through high school and it would sort of be a shame to let things die out and wither. Why don't we form a very loose organization, with no officers or dues; the only purpose would be to meet once a year, and have a good time." That was twenty-nine years ago. Up until about a year ago, we have been meeting at irregular intervals. The only reason that things more or less broke up is that the couple who were the "spark plug" of our group were divorced. I think, however, that twenty-nine years is sort of a record for this kind of thing.

To get back to my days in high school, I cannot overemphasize how enjoyable they were. During the last term of high school, there was a special "extracurricular" class which was intended to give students some practice at taking scholarship examinations. Attendance was open to anyone. I attended the class simply because I felt I had to win a scholarship if I were to get to college at all. The class was a lot of fun. We went into all our high school courses in a little more depth than was covered in a normal course. I believe an attempt is made to design most of these "scholarship" tests so that an adequate preparation cannot be made. Since there is still no agreement as to whether or not you can study to affect the results of these tests, I believe I would be very wise to drop the discussion right here.

The day for the test finally came. I can still remember, we were given a scholastic aptitude test in the morning and a scholastic achievement test in the afternoon. We were all competing for one of the so-called Mayor's Scholarships. They were called that because the city had a long time before ceded a piece of land to the University of Pennsylvania, and the University, in turn, granted nineteen four-year scholarships to the city of Philadelphia. These four-year scholarships were of great importance to the students. I took the test, but I did not "hold my breath" until something happened.

At this point, my thoughts about going to college were approximately as follows: I thought it rather unlikely that I would get a scholarship; the tuition at the University of Pennsylvania was, for those times, rather high – $400 a year, while the tuition costs at another college in Philadelphia – namely, Temple University – were only $200 a year. If I had any hopes at all of going to college, I thought I would probably go to Temple. But since I would not be going to college, it would be wise for me to start working in my father's jeweler shop.

After I had prepared for and taken the examination for the Mayor's Scholarship, graduation from high school came around. At the graduation, I heard, with envy, announcements that friends of mine had been awarded scholarships to various colleges. This envy disappeared as I went to work in my father's shop, learning the "jeweler's trade." One day, I got a phone call from a friend who said that my name was in the newspaper in a list of people who had been awarded scholarships. My father was so happy that he gave me the rest of the day off. My thoughts of trying to go to Temple University were, now, somewhat changed.

Once in college, I had the very definite feeling that I was

being swept along by events. But these events were so very pleasant, that I had not the least desire to complain. In my first college year, I took chemistry because I had a vague idea that I might want to be a chemistry teacher. The next year, I took physics because I thought I might want to be a physics teacher. I thought it was only proper to give both subjects a fair try. After two years of this "fair try," it was obvious that physics was far more to my liking than was chemistry. I have never since regretted that decision. As graduation approached, it was finally decided that I would be a candidate for a Bachelor's Degree, with an Honors Major in physics.

World War II was in full swing toward the end of my undergraduate days. The University of Pennsylvania had a subcontract with the Massachusetts Institute of Technology on the development of crystal rectifiers. These crystal rectifiers are an essential part of a radar set. It has been said that the speedy and sure development of radar in the United States turned the Battle of Britain. Before graduation, I was working at the University of Pennsylvania physics department in the crystal research section. Work on this project was considered important enough so that deferrments from military service were granted. This "war work" was a painless and gradual introduction into graduate work. After my undergraduate graduation, I slipped rather naturally into graduate work at the University of Pennsylvania. Graduate school in the physics department was, again, very pleasant. All graduate students, at that time, were given a desk and a room. There were three other fellows in my room. Our job, down in the labs on the crystal research project lasted from 9 in the morning until 5 at night. Most classes were held at night, and most studying was done in between the classes and at night.

In order to save myself an hour's journey by public transportation from my parents' home down to the

University and back each day, I rented a room down near the University.

After I had moved downtown to within walking distance of the university, I was, so to speak, "on my own." Every morning, I would get up and go down to the local Horn and Hardardt Restaurant to have breakfast. Having breakfast at the local H and H was an experience for me. This was a cafeteria-type restaurant, and every morning, I would see people in front of me ordering scrambled eggs and "home fried potatoes." Now I knew from my mother that the human body could not take "home fried potatoes" for breakfast. The reason was simply that "civilized people don't do such things." Still common courtesy required me to allow these people to enjoy what was probably going to be their last meal. When the same people came in on following days and ordered the same "poison," I thought there might be some delay in their punishment – a delay that my mother had forgotten to tell me aobut. But there was no doubt in my mind but that the punishment for these "innocents" would come eventually.

After about half a year, during which these people kept coming back and getting more "home fried potatoes," it occurred to me that perhaps the original premise was wrong. Maybe it was possible to eat "home fried potatoes" for breakfast and still survive. (I want you to know that this is a very big step to take – to begin to doubt the things you learned at your mother's knee.) At any rate, I eventually decided that if it didn't hurt them, perhaps it wouldn't hurt me either. Finally one day, I ordered scrambled eggs and home fried potatoes for breakfast for myself. I admit that it was with fear and trepidation that I tasted the potatoes. By gosh, they were good! They were so good that they soon became my standard breakfast.

And so, another old wives' tale bites the dust!

Finally, V-E Day came around, and we, as well as the rest of the University, had a big celebration. I remember that celebration very well because that was the first day that I noticed a symptom which in retrospect was the first symptom I had of MS. Specifically, I remember lying on the grass in Wissahickon Park and looking up at the leaves in a tree. I'm not quite sure how I happened to come to observe this, but vision with my right eye was far more clear than was the vision of the same scene with my left eye. This effect, coming as closely as it did on the heels of a bout with dysarthria, and some difficulty in writing, would almost certainly be a warning sign to a "sharp" neurologist. But I was not yet seeing a neurologist, much less a "sharp" one, so all these symptoms went unheeded. I still don't know what could have been done if they had been heeded, but that's beside the point.

I was 26 years old at the time, and I should probably date the onset of the disease, but not the diagnosis, from then. My symptoms were all of a transitory nature, and I would have classified myself, at that time, as being in good health. It was about that time that I got married, and it seemed perfectly natural to me to take out an insurance policy on my life. The policy that I took required a medical examination; with no effort at all, I passed that medical examination.

As I have tried to imply several times before, it takes a very trained and skillful eye to detect MS in its very early stages.

Shortly after I graduated from high school and college was a sure thing, we (my parents and I) decided that working in my father's shop was not really the wisest of all possible courses. In fact, it might be a good idea to take a job where I could earn a little bit more money – "pin" money for minor emergencies. So it happened, that I became a Fuller brush man. The manager of our section took me out on the first day in order to show me how to sell Fuller brushes. He chose a house, apparently at random, and after gaining admission, went into his "spiel." He explained my presence to the lady of the house by telling her that I was his "supervisor." The lady of the house might have had too many other things on her mind to realize how ridiculous it was to have a young, high school kid be the supervisor of an older and more polished salesman.

My teacher/manager used tactics which would have been the pride of any commando outfit, and the manager was soon in the living room, displaying his wares. He spoke interminably of the excellence of the various Fuller products, and finally the lady gave him a very sizable order for brushes – over $10 as I recall now. I still don't know whether the lady ordered the brushes because she wanted and needed them or because that seemed to be the only way she could "call off" this pestiferous salesman.

I was a failure as a Fuller brush salesman. Nowadays, I think the reason is that I am totally obsessed with the idea of deciding for myself, that the idea of trying to convince other people that yours is the only way is simply abhorrent.

Before going on with this story, I must digress for a moment. (If you are counting the number of times I have digressed, I suggest that this is a very futile thing to do. One of my most outstanding characteristics is that I "digress" frequently, but most of the time, I do get back to the main subject eventually.) In my senior year of high school, I had a physics course, and my instructor was Dr. Waldie. One day, in physics class, we did an experiment involving electrical wires, and at the end of the experiment, I had apparently neglected to coil the wires up neatly and put them back in the drawer. (As an adult, or parent, I would be the first to agree that this would be a very desirable thing to do.) On that particular day, Dr. Waldie happened to notice the wire simply thrown in the drawer, rather than neatly coiled. She knew that I was responsible for this, and she reprimanded me sternly, saying, "Greenblatt, you'll never get to college. And, if by some freak chance you should get there, you won't last more than half a year." At this time, of course, I was thinking of going to college but had no real idea of whether I would be able to or not. Several months later, I had gotten my scholarship to the University of Pennsylvania, and I was trying to earn a few extra dollars during the summer by selling Fuller brushes. At one of the houses where I rang the doorbell and tried to sell some of the brushes, the lady of the house happened to have a house guest, and the guest was none other then my teacher, Dr. Waldie! My meekness and kind manners quickly gained admission to the living room, and Dr. Waldie and I greeted each other. She was unaware of the fact that I had been admitted to college. I don't know what thoughts ran through Dr. Waldie's mind, but it may have been something similar to the following: "Oh, my goodness! Greenblatt was such a fine, promising young man, I wonder if I was a little bit too harsh with him, telling him that he would never make it to college and that he would be expelled within half a year. It seems a pity that he never even had a chance to try."

11

Smoking and Weight Problems

I STARTED smoking sometime around 1940. Since the time that I started smoking, my consumption of cigarettes went up to a level of one carton (approximately 10 packs) per week. My cigarette smoking started in the blissful days when cigarettes cost only about 13¢ per pack. Every few years, the price of cigarettes would be increased by a penny or so per pack; and simultaneously, one would hear comments from the smoking community to the effect that "I'm not goin' to pay that extra penny or two. I'm goin' to quit smokin.' " When the price passed 20¢ per pack, I joined the complainers and swore that I, too, was going to give up smoking. But each time, the same thing that happens to most people, happened to me. I complained for a few days and then gently settled into a new routine smoking perhaps more and paying more for it.

There are two distinct schools of thought when it comes to quitting smoking. There is, first, the school of "the easiest way is to taper off." For every one who believes that one can successfully taper off, there are those who believe, just as vehemently, that the only way to quit is to quit entirely – all at once.

Each time the price of cigarettes went up, I tried one or the other of these two methods to quit smoking cigarettes, but neither method was successful. I actually began to believe that if you did succeed in stopping smoking, some sort of a terrible disease would be sure to strike you. Because of this conviction, knowing full-well it was ridiculous, it was not hard to settle back into the well-worn channel of cigarette smoking.

In the year 1956, a fortunate accident happened, and I would like to tell about it. One night I ran out of cigarettes around 9 o'clock. My wife happened to be out of the house with the car, and since the nearest candy store was several miles away, it wasn't practical for me to go out and buy another pack. Since my wife Nora also smoked, I decided that I would be just as well off if I were to wait for her to come home. So I waited for her. Those few hours without any cigarettes were agony, but they were bearable because I knew Nora would have some cigarettes with her. When Nora finally did come home around 11:15, I was dismayed to learn that she also had run out of cigarettes. All candy stores in the town of Princeton would be closed at that hour. There was nothing I could do but bury my sadness in sleep.

Somehow, I managed to fall asleep that night. My agony of the night before was as nothing compared with the fact that I had to wake up the next morning without cigarettes. Worse than that, I even had breakfast and didn't have a cigarette afterward! But somehow, I managed to survive these difficulties primarily by thinking that soon I would be at the Laboratories where there was a cigarette machine. I don't remember exactly what happened when I got to the Laboratories, but the situation was such that I couldn't get near the cigarette machine for about two hours. At 10:30, however, I made my way down to the machine and was all set to pop my quarter into the machine when I suddenly realized, "Hey, look, fella, it is now 13 hours since you had your last cigarette, and you are not dead. Why don't you try to hold off a bit more and see how long this can last?" So I tried to see how long it would last, and by my watch I see it is now some 13 years, 7 months, 14 days and 3 hours. I suspect that this abstinence can be carried even further.

At the time I quite smoking, I weighed 193 pounds. After I quit smoking, I found, as do so many others, that my weight started to go up and up and up. At this point, I said to myself, "Look here, Greenblatt. (That's a name that I often use to address myself when speaking to myself.) If you have enough gumption to give up smoking, I'm sure you must have the wherewithal to do some weight-losing." After considering the various methods of losing weight and rejecting the quickest method – namely, amputation – I decided to follow the recommendations given in a book for weight-losing written by a Dr. Jolliffe. According to Dr. Jolliffe's book, one could calculate a certain daily caloric requirement which depends on sex, age, weight and occupation. I estimated that my daily caloric requirement was about 2400 calories. According to Dr. Jolliffe's book, each 3000 or so calories of carbohydrates were equivalent to about one pound of body weight. Also, each 1900 or so calories of protein were also the equivalent of one pound of body weight. But even though starving yourself of protein only is a very efficient way of losing weight, it is also a very poor method because it exposes you unnecessarily to a great many diseases including rickets and scurvy. So I went on what I thought was a well-balanced diet of about 1900 calories a day. My caloric deficit was approximately, therefore, 500 calories a day. Since this deficit was both in carbohydrates and in proteins, I figured the average would be about 2500 calories per pound of body weight. At this rate, I ought to lose about 1½ pounds per week. I was very pleased that even with such approximation, this figure was just about right. Within a matter of two months, I had lost about 15 pounds. The important thing, as Dr. Jolliffe points out, is that one must maintain the new lower weight for several months in order to give the stomach a chance to shrink to its new size. If one doesn't give the stomach a chance to shrink, then one will get hungry often and the weight will come back, much like the proverbial "bad penny." I have always been proud of the fact that by reading that book and by following the directions therein rather carefully I was able to lose weight – something that so many friends of mine have been apparently unable to do.

12

My Philosophy

WHEN I first thought of this book, this chapter was not included. But after I finished the preceding chapters and showed them to a few friends, they were unanimously of the opinion that I should have included something about how I, personally, have managed to retain a fairly active life in spite of MS. At first I blushed when they suggested that I should write something about my philosophy of life. I knew perfectly well that I was not a philosopher, and I thought it was rather presumptuous to think that anything I had written could be called a "philosophy." But then I realized that one doesn't have to be a philosopher in order to have a philosophy of life. In essence, the philosophy I am talking about is simply a way of looking at things. As I thought about it more and more, I decided that possibly the best way to indicate my attitude might be to give quotations from other people and to tell why I am fond of them. One of my favorite quotations is entitled "The Serenity Prayer":

The Serenity Prayer

> God grant me the serenity to accept the things I cannot change, the courage to change those things I can, and the wisdom to tell the difference.
>
> R. Niebuhr

I am fond of the philosophy implied in this prayer because it recognizes that some things can be changed and others cannot; it also recognizes that not everybody has the ability to tell what can and what cannot be changed. This phrase has been adopted by the organization Alcoholics Anonymous. If it hadn't been preempted by that group, I would strongly urge that the phrase be adopted by MS patients. Another favorite quotation of mine is the following:

> No man is an island, entire of itself. . . .
>
> John Donne

This quotation, which ends with the words "never send to know for whom the bell tolls; it tolls for thee," points out the dependency of each man on his neighbor and I subscribe heartily to that philosophy. The following is another short but significant quotation:

> Humor is an affirmation of dignity, a declaration of man's superiority to all that befalls him.
>
> Romain Gary

I think that last comment almost speaks for itself.

In addition to the three quotations given above, there are the wonderful statements included in the Bible in the Sermon on the Mount. I have always been impressed by this phrase:

> Let him who among you who is without sin cast the first stone.

This statement seems, to me, to be a simple recognition of the fact that all of us have sinned to some degree or another. Its message is just beautiful, and, of course, a statement like the Golden Rule needs no comment at all.

Other statements to which I subscribe wholeheartedly are the following. Around the inside of the rotunda of the Jefferson Memorial in Washington is inscribed the following statement:

> I swear, upon the alter of God, eternal hostility to all forms of tyranny over the minds of men.
>
> Thomas Jefferson

I first saw this statement on the inside of the Jefferson Memorial when I happened to visit Washington way, way back in the 1940's. Part of the reason that I remember it might be that my friend and I got to the Memorial shortly after 5 o'clock, and it was closed. The statement is inscribed around the full circumference of the Memorial. We were able to read it, a part at a time, by walking around the Memorial and looking in through the Colonnade. It was a very torturous way to read the inscription, but the meaning of the inscription was worth far more than the trouble in reading it. Here is another quotation of which I am fond:

> Tolerance toward intolerance ought be considered a vice rather than a virtue.

I don't know who is responsible for that last statement but I certainly agree with it.

These quotations reflect my feelings and attitudes concerning relationships between people, and they are part of my philosophy of life.

A WHEELCHAIR PHILOSOPHY

In 1959, I was a bit unsteady on my feet, but I always managed to get where I was going. I still did not use a cane, a crutch or any other device. On July 1 of that year, I transferred from the RCA Laboratories to the RCA Space Division. The RCA Space Division was not yet in existence; in fact, they merely rented some space from another industrial outfit. There was no cafeteria at the plant yet. The only eating facility they had was a special room set aside for a large array of vending machines. These machines dispensed sandwiches, ice cream, various beverages, soups and so forth.

On my first day there, I wandered into this "machine room," just to see how I would fare with these machines. Since my gait was relatively unsteady, I decided then that it would be better for me to eat my lunch while standing up in the machine room, rather than risk a journey all the way back to my desk. Since it was lunch time, there were a goodly number of people in the room. (I am sure they didn't come specifically to watch me, but I felt that every eye was glued upon me as I tried to buy my lunch.) I tried to be as nonchalant as possible as I put my nickles into the soft drink machine. I am beginning to suspect that machines are sadistically inclined, because this one dropped the cup upside down, and "my" coke began to pour on the bottom of the cup. I've seen able-bodied men fail to save more than a few drops of a precious liquid when this happens, so what do you suppose a person like myself could do! You're right, I helplessly watched as the beautiful liquid ran down the drain, but I got even! I kicked the machine and thus drew even more attention to my pathetic attempts.

But I was no quitter. Even though I had been very obviously defeated in this encounter with the machine, I had more nickles and was willing to try another machine. I sauntered with a gay outward look (but with heart pounding inside me) over to an ice cream machine. Here again, I moved the controls to the appropriate positions and dropped my nickles in. Now one experienced in this game might ask himself, "What can possibly go wrong in an ice cream machine?" I haven't made a study of the different things that can go wrong, but this one simply did nothing. It didn't even acknowledge that I was there. In fact, I thought I could hear the machine laughing to itself. But perhaps that was my imagination. I would consider myself a fool if, after having lost twice to two different machines, I would still continue to try to get some food. After that sad experience (I almost starved that afternoon), I would ask a friend to get some refreshments for me.

In November of that year, I got myself a cane. Shortly after I started to use the cane, I happened to come across a statement (in *Barlett's Quotations)* made by Governor Al Smith. He made this statement in his speech on behalf of Franklin D. Roosevelt, who was running for governor of New York in 1928. Some of the detracters of FDR were apparently decrying the fact that he had to use a cane and leg braces, and Smith, in his speech, said, "The Governor of New York State does not have to be an acrobat." Recognition of the fact that one's physical prowess doesn't have much to do with one's intellectual abilities has kept me going.

Index